C.S. PACAT   JOHANNA THE MAD   JOANA LAFUENTE

FENCE™

VOLUME ONE

BOOM!
BOX™

BOOM! BOX™

FENCE Volume One DISCOVER NOW EDITION, April 2018. Published by BOOM! Box, a division of Boom Entertainment, Inc. Fence is ™ & © 2018 C.S. Pacat. Originally published in single magazine form as FENCE No. 1-4. ™ & © 2017, 2018 C.S. Pacat. All rights reserved. BOOM! Box™ and the BOOM! Box logo are trademarks of Boom Entertainment, Inc., registered in various countries and categories. All characters, events, and institutions depicted herein are fictional. Any similarity between any of the names, characters, persons, events, and/or institutions in this publication to actual names, characters, and persons, whether living or dead, events, and/or institutions is unintended and purely coincidental. BOOM! Box does not read or accept unsolicited submissions of ideas, stories, or artwork.

For information regarding the CPSIA on this printed material, call: (203) 595-3636 and provide reference #RICH – 779492.

BOOM! Studios, 5670 Wilshire Boulevard, Suite 400, Los Angeles, CA 90036-5679. Printed in USA. First Printing.

ISBN: 978-1-68415-174-5, eISBN: 978-1-64144-098-1

WRITTEN BY
C.S. Pacat

ILLUSTRATED BY
Johanna the Mad

COLORS BY
Joana LaFuente

LETTERS BY
Jim Campbell

TECHNICAL CONSULTANT
Pieter Leeuwenburgh

SCHOOL LOGO DESIGNS
Fawn Lau

COVER BY
Shanen Pae

SERIES DESIGNER
Marie Krupina

COLLECTION DESIGNER
Kara Leopard

EDITORS
Shannon Watters & Dafna Pleban

CREATED BY
C.S. Pacat & Johanna the Mad

THEY SAY THE TIP OF A FENCER'S BLADE IS THE FASTEST THING AT THE OLYMPICS, OTHER THAN THE MARKSMAN'S *BULLET.*

WATCHING FROM THE SIDELINES, IT JUST LOOKS LIKE A *BLUR.*

THAT'S HOW QUICKLY YOU CAN WIN OR LOSE.

August 8, 1984

ROBERT COSTE WINS GOLD FOR USA

—OLYMPIC VICTORY IN LA—

Robert Coste beat out Boisaggo 4-10 in a historic final, winning USA's first ever Olympic gold in épée.

No other American fencer has scored a gold at the Olympics besides Post, who won a 1904 victory in singlestick, a now discontinued event.

Wednesday's win continues an impressive win streak for the 21-year-old Coste, who came to the event as the reigning world champion after wining the title at World Championships in Vienna to the épée team

IN AN *INSTANT.*

CONNECTICUT REGIONAL CIRCUIT
2018 SEASON

NAME?

SIGN IN

JOE
ÉPÉE COACH (part time)

YEAH. WHY?

IS HE GOOD?

YOU LIKE SHORT TOURNAMENTS?

HOW CAN WEAPONS CHECK TAKE TWO HOURS? *ALL* THE MORNING BOUTS ARE RUNNING BEHIND.

I HEARD THAT AT WORLDS, THEY DO WEAPONS CHECK THE NIGHT BEFORE, IN THE HOTEL.

KYLE, WE ALL ALREADY KNOW YOUR COUSIN COMPETED AT WORLDS.

"MY COUSIN SAYS THAT AT WORLDS..."

"DID I EVER TELL YOU ABOUT THE TIME AT WORLDS..."

I'M JUST SAYING TALENT RUNS IN MY FAMILY.

HEY, KYLE, RAHUL. CHECK OUT THAT GUY.

HEH. THERE'S ALWAYS SOMEONE FROM A CRAPPY LOCAL CLUB WHO TURNS UP THINKING THEY CAN WIN A TOURNAMENT.

MY FIRST MEET. DISTRICT ONE, INDIVIDUAL ÉPÉE.

ALL THE ROUNDS ARE SUDDEN DEATH ROUNDS. ONE LOSS AND YOU'RE OUT.

IT'S NOT LIKE FENCING BACK HOME.

IT'S A ROOM FULL OF RIVALS, LOOKING FOR WEAKNESS.

THEY DON'T KNOW ME, AND I DON'T KNOW THEM.

BUT I KNOW ONE THING.

THOSE SHOES LOOK LIKE THEY CAME FROM GOODWILL.

I KNOW I CAN FENCE.

THEY'RE GOOD ENOUGH TO BEAT *YOU*.

LEAVE IT. HE'S NOT MAKING IT PAST FIRST ROUND. HE'S THE ONE FENCING SEIJI.

YOU'RE FENCING SEIJI?

YOU'RE ALREADY DEAD.

METAPHORICALLY. *PROBABLY.*

NICE KNOWING YOU.

WHAT'S SO GOOD ABOUT THIS SEIJI GUY, ANYWAY?

YOU DON'T KNOW WHO SEIJI IS?

SHUT UP, HE'S COMING!

OH MY GOD, IT'S REALLY HIM. IT'S--

IT WAS SO FAST. FASTER THAN COACH JOE.

I DIDN'T EVEN SEE IT COMING.

YOU LIKE THE SWORD AND JACKET?

HOW MUCH IS IT?

HOW MUCH YOU GOT?

THAT AIN'T ENOUGH, KID.

I THOUGHT, MAYBE I COULD HELP OUT AROUND THE PLACE, IN EXCHANGE FOR LESSONS.

YOU WANT FREE LESSONS?

JOE'S FENCING
FRIDAYS
SALSA
THURSDAYS

I WORK HARD. I COULD CLEAN THE GRAFFITI, PATCH UP THAT WALL--

I DON'T GIVE FREE LESSONS.

SALSA WINTER SEASON

NOT SUCH A TIGHT GRIP! HOLD IT LIKE A BIRD. YOU DON'T WANT IT TO FLY AWAY. BUT DON'T KILL IT EITHER.

RELAX YOUR UPPER BODY. IF YOU TENSE YOUR SHOULDER LIKE THAT BEFORE YOU ATTACK, I'LL SEE IT COMING.

NOW DISENGAGE AND LUNGE, LUNGE-- YES!

LISTEN KID, YOU'VE GOT REAL POTENTIAL.

IF YOU WON ONE OF THE LOCAL TOURNAMENTS...

...GOT NOTICED BY ONE OF THE HIGH SCHOOL VARSITY COACHES...

YOU COULD WIN A SCHOLARSHIP AND GET SOME REAL COACHING.

BETTER THAN I CAN GIVE YOU.

REGISTRATION FEE IS $65?!

PLUS A $20 ADMIN FEE.

PLUS BUS FARE...

bills

FIFTEEN-ZERO. INCREDIBLE.

SEIJI'S UNTOUCHABLE.

I'M JUST GLAD HE'S NOT IN MY BRACKET.

HE TOTALLY HUMILIATED THAT OTHER GUY. WHAT WAS HIS NAME?

WHO CARES.

YOU WANNA GET TACOS WHEN WE'RE DONE?

SURE!

EXCELLENT WORK, SEIJI.

OF COURSE, THE CALIBRE OF FENCING WILL BE HIGHER WHEN YOU START NEXT YEAR AT EXTON--

HEY, YOU! SEIJI OR WHATEVER--

ARE YOU JUST GOING TO IGNORE ME?

WHAT DO YOU WANT, ZERO?

ZERO

EVERYONE SAYS THAT.

YOU MAY BE UNTOUCHABLE, BUT I'M GOING TO BE THE ONE WHO BREAKS THROUGH YOUR GUARD.

I'M GOING TO *BEAT YOU,* AND YOU'RE GOING TO KNOW WHAT IT FEELS LIKE TO LOSE OUT THERE IN FRONT OF EVERYONE.

THAT'S TRUE. I SAID THAT.

I SAID IT LAST YEAR.

I SAID IT AT THE UNDER 14s.

DIDN'T YOU SAY IT TO HIM LAST TIME HE FENCED YOU?

LIKE EIGHT TIMES.

I DON'T LOOK BACK AT GUYS WHO'VE LOST.

BEAT ME AT YOUR SKILL LEVEL?

KINGS ROW BOYS SCHOOL

KINGS ROW ISN'T A TOP FENCING SCHOOL, AND THEY'VE NEVER WON A STATE CHAMPIONSHIP.

BUT I DON'T CARE ABOUT ANY OF THAT.

YOU CAN SEND FOR THE REST OF YOUR THINGS AFTER YOU SETTLE IN.

DORMITORY - CASTELLO

THIS IS EVERYTHING.

OH. WELL, DON'T WORRY. WE TAKE ONE SCHOLARSHIP STUDENT PER YEAR, SO YOU WON'T FEEL OUT OF PLACE DUE TO YOUR ECONOMIC CIRCUMSTANCES.

OF COURSE, YOUR SCHOLARSHIP IS DEPENDENT ON YOUR MAKING THE TEAM.

I KNOW THAT.

I'M HERE TO MAKE THE TEAM, AND FENCE AGAINST EXTON.

BECAUSE THERE'S SOMEONE AT THAT SCHOOL I NEED TO BEAT.

HERE WE ARE, ROOM 108.

108

YOUR ROOMMATE'S TRYING OUT FOR THE TEAM TOO, SO YOU'LL HAVE SOMETHING IN COMMON.

HUH? WE FENCED AT REGIONALS.

YOU WERE THE FAVORITE, I WAS THE UP-AND-COMER.

AND I CAME *THIS CLOSE* TO LANDING...

...ONE POINT...

...OKAY, BUT IT WAS STILL SOMEHOW A BIG DEAL.

SO YOU ACTUALLY LOST FIFTEEN-ZERO?

WE DON'T KNOW EACH OTHER. HE'S JUST SOME FENCER I BEAT AT REGIONALS.

I AM NOT *SOME FENCER.*

MY NAME'S NICHOLAS COX.

AND I'M GOING TO MAKE YOU REMEMBER IT.

IT WOULD BE WEIRD NOT TO REMEMBER THE NAME OF YOUR OWN ROOMMATE.

THAT'S NOT WHAT I MEANT.

I MEANT THAT I'M COMING FOR Y--

I KNOW WHAT YOU MEANT. YOU'RE ONE OF THOSE.

ONE OF WHAT?

UNFOUNDED CONFIDENCE.

CAN'T LAND A POINT, BUT THINKS HE CAN TAKE ME AT NATIONALS.

LET ME GUESS. SOMEONE TOLD YOU ONCE THAT YOU HAD POTENTIAL.

YOU HAVEN'T FIGURED OUT YET THAT HUNDREDS OF FENCERS GET TOLD THAT.

IT'S NOT LIKE YOU WON AT NATIONALS. YOU LOST.

YOU'RE NOT INVINCIBLE.

YOU GOT BEAT JUST LIKE EVERYONE ELSE.

SHUT UP, ZERO.

DON'T CALL ME THAT!

I'M NOT ROOMING WITH HIM!

HEY, HEY. IF YOU'VE GOT A PROBLEM WITH ROOMS, TAKE IT UP WITH COACH IN THE MORNING.

FOR TONIGHT, MAKE IT WORK.

DID YOU REALLY TELL THEM TO TAKE IT UP WITH COACH?

THE CAPTAIN SHOWS NO REMORSE.

ARE THESE THE MATCH-UPS FOR THE TEAM TRYOUTS?

I HAVE A SYSTEM.

SEIJI KATAYAMA...

...SO IT'S TRUE. YOU'RE REALLY AIMING US AT THE STATE CHAMPIONSHIP THIS YEAR.

YOU THINK WITH SEIJI ON THE TEAM, WE CAN BEAT EXTON.

NO.

SEIJI CAN'T BEAT EXTON THE WAY HE IS NOW.

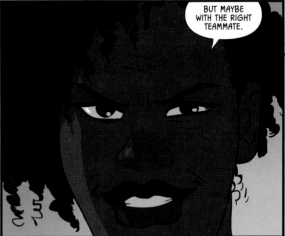

BUT MAYBE WITH THE RIGHT TEAMMATE.

YOU'RE LOOKING FOR THE FENCING SALLE, RIGHT? *UM.* IT'S BACK THIS WAY. I CAN TELL FROM YOUR SPORTS BAG!

THANKS, I TOOK A WRONG TURN.

WAS IT A JOCK WITH HAIR LIKE--

"THAT'S EUGENE LABAO, HE'S A JUNIOR.

"DON'T TAKE IT PERSONALLY! EVERYONE GETS COMPETITIVE DURING TRYOUTS.

"ALTHOUGH EUGENE'S PRETTY MUCH ALWAYS COMPETITIVE."

I'M BOBBY.

NICHOLAS.

YOU ROOM WITH SEIJI, RIGHT?

RIGHT.

WHAT'S HE LIKE, YOU KNOW, IN PERSON?

HE'S WORSE IN PERSON.

Bobby Vision

Nicholas Vision

SEIJI!

YOU WANNA TALK TO HIM? I CAN INTRODUCE YOU.

EXCEPT HE'LL PROBABLY BE A HUGE JERK.

AND CRUSH THIS GUY'S DREAMS.

I'M SO FAR AHEAD OF YOU I'M SURPRISED YOU CAN SEE ME AT ALL.

SEIJI!

AAHA, N-NO THAT'S OKAY, I MEAN, I'M REALLY SHY, SO...

OKAY, WELL. HIS LOSS.

WHAT WAS YOUR WIN-LOSS LAST SEASON?

I WAS 39-1.

AND YOUR RANKING?

SECOND.

BEHIND *JESSE COSTE*, RIGHT?

THAT'S RIGHT.

JESSE COSTE IS THE TEAM CAPTAIN OVER AT EXTON.

"JESSE'S RANKED NUMBER ONE IN THE COUNTRY IN INDIVIDUAL ÉPÉE.

"HE'S THE ONE WHO TOOK OUT SEIJI AT NATIONALS LAST YEAR IN THE SEMI FINAL."

YOU'VE HEARD OF THE OLYMPIC CHAMPION ROBERT COSTE?

JESSE'S HIS SON.

HIS *LEGITIMATE* SON.

JESSE COSTE IS A FENCING PRODIGY!

HE'S HAD THE BEST TRAINERS AND INSTRUCTION SINCE HE WAS FIVE.

PLUS, HIS FATHER IS HIS PERSONAL COACH.

LET ME GUESS, YOU THINK WITH YOU ON THE TEAM, WE CAN BEAT EXTON?

NO.

"EXTON RECRUITS THE TOP FENCERS IN THE COUNTRY.

"KINGS ROW HAS A THIRD RATE TEAM, WITHOUT ANY OUTSTANDING FENCERS."

YOUR CAPTAIN'S THE ONLY ONE HERE WHO'S RANKED IN THE TOP FIFTY.

YOU ARROGANT LITTLE--

COOL IT, TANNER.

HEY, COME ON. LET'S GO WARM UP.

I SAW YOU AT NATIONALS. YOU'VE GOT A GOOD PARRY SIX.

ANYONE WHO WENT 39-1 WOULD BE AN ASSET TO THIS TEAM.

IF I MAKE THE TEAM, ONE OF YOUR FRIENDS WILL BE SENT BACK TO RESERVES.

I KNOW THAT. SO DO THEY.

OF COURSE, THE TEAM HASN'T BEEN DECIDED YET.

NICHOLAS!

ÉPÉE. THE SWORD OF DUELISTS--

--ALTHOUGH OF COURSE *SABER* IS BETTER, WITH ITS HIGH SPEED ATTACKS, THE JOY OF HITTING WITH THE EDGE OF THE BLADE--

SABER IS NOT BETTER.

WHAT JUST HAPPENED?

ISN'T SHE AN ÉPÉE COACH?

COACH WILLIAMS' RULES. YOU SAY ANYTHING ON THE WALL, YOU DO TWO HUNDRED SUICIDES.

TWO HUNDRED?!

YEP.

"AIDEN DUMPED ME"

WHO'S AIDEN?

"WE MADE IT TO THE FINALS ONCE, IN 1979.

"THAT YEAR, ROBERT COSTE WAS A STUDENT HERE. HE WENT ON TO WIN OLYMPIC GOLD."

ROBERT COSTE WAS A STUDENT HERE!

BUT EVEN ONE EXTRAORDINARY FENCER IS NOT ENOUGH TO WIN A STATE TITLE.

THAT TAKES A TEAM.

AND FOR THE LAST TEN YEARS, THE STATE FINALS HAVE BEEN DOMINATED BY ONE TEAM ONLY.

"EXTON."

"WITH JESSE COSTE AS THEIR CAPTAIN, THEY HOST SOME OF THE BEST FENCERS IN THE COUNTRY.

"YOUR PAST COACHES HAVE TOLD YOU THAT YOU CAN'T BEAT THEM."

I'M HERE TO TELL YOU THAT WE CAN.

AND WE WILL.

WE'RE GOING TO TAKE ON EXTON.

WE'RE GOING TO BEAT THEM.

AND WE'RE GOING TO **WIN** THE STATE CHAMPIONSHIP.

SOMEWHERE IN THIS ROOM ARE THE THREE BOYS WHO ARE GOING TO DO THAT.

YOU JUST HAVE TO ASK YOURSELF--

YOU WANT ME TO TELL COACH THAT WE KISSED AND MADE UP?

TELL HER WHATEVER YOU WANT.

I'LL HAVE THE ROOM TO MYSELF SOON.

WHAT'S THAT SUPPOSED TO MEAN?

YOUR SCHOLARSHIP DEPENDS ON YOU MAKING THE TEAM.

YOU'RE NOT GOING TO BE HERE LONG.

THREE WEEKS.

THAT'S HOW LONG WE HAVE BETWEEN NOW AND OUR FIRST STATE TOURNAMENT MATCH.

"IN THAT TIME I'LL PICK THE THREE BOYS WHO WILL FIT THE A, B, AND C SLOTS OF THE KINGS ROW VARSITY TEAM."

"WE'LL START WITH SOME SIMPLE EXERCISES TO TEST YOUR OVERALL ATHLETIC ABILITY."

FENCING ISN'T A SPORT OF STRENGTH LIKE WEIGHTLIFTING, OR A SPORT OF ENDURANCE LIKE RUNNING A MARATHON.

IT RELIES ON OTHER SKILLS.

TWENTY-SEVEN!

IT TOOK ME LONGER TO PRESS THE BUTTON ON THE STOPWATCH THAN IT DID FOR HIM TO HIT THE NUMBER.

GO, NICHOLAS! YOU CAN DO IT!

FOUR!

THERE!

HE SEES THE NUMBER RIGHT AWAY, BUT DOESN'T HAVE THE TECHNIQUE TO HIT IT.

ELEVEN!

SECOND FASTEST TIME AFTER SEIJI.

THIRTY-TWO!

ARE YOU SURE IT'S ON HERE? I CAN'T SEE IT ANYWHERE.

THE EXERCISES WE DO THIS WEEK ARE JUST TO GIVE ME AN IDEA OF YOUR WEAKNESSES AND STRENGTHS.

THE TEAM ITSELF WILL BE DECIDED BY TOURNAMENT.

YOU'LL FENCE ROUND ROBIN STYLE, SO EACH BOY WILL FENCE EVERY OTHER BOY IN TURN.

THE THREE BOYS WITH THE MOST WINS MAKE THE TEAM.

I'LL POST THE BOUT ORDER ON FRIDAY.

UNTIL THEN, GOOD LUCK. DISMISSED!

WHO D'YOU THINK YOUR FIRST MATCH WILL BE AGAINST?

I'D LIKE TO GET A WIN FIRST, SO I HOPE IT'S NOT SEIJI.

THAT WOULD BE SO DEMORALIZING!

MAYBE WE'LL GET TO FENCE AIDEN.

AIDEN!

NICHOLAS! YOU STAY BEHIND.

YOU'RE LEFT-HANDED.

THAT GIVES YOU AN ADVANTAGE, SINCE MOST FENCERS TRAIN AGAINST RIGHT-HANDED OPPONENTS.

AND YOU'RE FAST, WITH GOOD INSTINCTS. YOU CAN WIN A LOT OF BOUTS WITH THOSE THINGS ALONE.

BUT YOU'VE BEEN POORLY TRAINED, AND YOU'VE LEARNED A LOT OF BAD HABITS.

YOUR TECHNIQUE IS THE WEAKEST OF THE BOYS HERE.

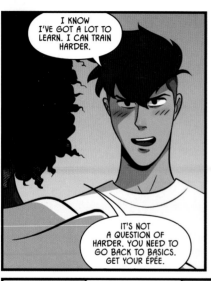

I KNOW I'VE GOT A LOT TO LEARN. I CAN TRAIN HARDER.

IT'S NOT A QUESTION OF HARDER. YOU NEED TO GO BACK TO BASICS. GET YOUR ÉPÉE.

EACH OF THE THREE WEAPONS IN FENCING HAS A DIFFERENT STYLE BASED ON ITS RULES AND ITS HISTORY.

SABER--TRULY THE GREATEST OF ALL WEAPONS, AND THE ONLY WEAPON THAT ALLOWS HITS WITH THE EDGE OF THE BLADE...

AREN'T YOU AN ÉPÉE COACH, THOUGH?

FOIL

Target area is the torso only. Hits outside the torso do not score a point.

SABER

Target area is the torso, arms and head. Hits on the legs or hands do not score a point.

"FOIL AND SABER HAVE RESTRICTED TARGET AREAS. A HIT DOESN'T SCORE UNLESS IT LANDS WITHIN THE TARGET AREA."

...FOIL, WITH ITS LIGHTER, MORE FLEXIBLE BLADE AND PRECISE RULES GOVERNING RIGHT OF WAY--

ÉPÉE

Target area = everywhere.

"--BUT IN ÉPÉE, YOUR WHOLE BODY IS A TARGET.

"A HIT SCORES IF IT LANDS ON YOUR TORSO, YOUR HEAD, YOUR KNEE, YOUR HAND, EVEN YOUR TOE."

...AND OUR WEAPON. ÉPÉE. SOMETIMES CALLED THE SWORD OF DUELISTS BECAUSE ITS RULES MOST CLOSELY RESEMBLE REAL COMBAT.

LET'S SEE YOUR BASIC STANCE. EN GARDE.

Correct wrist position is straight, leaving no line of attack open to forearm.

YOUR WRIST IS BENT. YOUR FOREARM IS VULNERABLE.

Potential hit to forearm

Potential hit to back

A good stance is a little "side on" to protect the back.

YOUR STANCE IS TOO SIDE ON. YOU'LL EXPOSE YOUR BACK.

YOU LEAN FORWARD TOO MUCH WHEN YOU LUNGE. YOUR HEAD IS VULNERABLE.

When lunging, the torso remains upright, allowing a swift return to stance.

BUT YOUR WORST HABIT IS THAT YOU STEP BEFORE YOU EXTEND YOUR SWORD ARM TO ATTACK.

THAT'S HOW SEIJI SCORED ALL THOSE POINTS ON YOU AT REGIONALS, DESPITE YOUR AGGRESSIVE INSTINCTS AND NATURAL SPEED.

YES...I SAW THAT MATCH.

HE BEAT YOU UTTERLY.

HE'S HAD YEARS OF TRAINING.

SO THE QUESTION IS, CAN YOU CATCH UP?

YOU TOO, HUH?

"SHORT ARMS AND LACK OF CONFIDENCE."

"WORST TECHNIQUE IN THE CLASS."

YOU CAN IMPROVE TECHNIQUE.

YOU CAN COMPENSATE FOR A SHORT REACH.

OR STRETCH MY ARMS.

HEY, BOBBY. WHY DO YOU WANT TO BE A FENCER?

FENCING IS COOL! THE WEAPONS ARE COOL, THE UNIFORMS ARE COOL, THE PEOPLE ARE COOL--

"I GUESS IT'S ABOUT THE KIND OF PERSON I WANT TO BE.

"SOMEONE WHO CAN ACCOMPLISH THEIR GOALS."

WHAT ABOUT YOU?

TAK TAK TAK TAK TAK TAK

SEIJI, WHO IS THIS BOY? YOU KNOW I DON'T LIKE INTERRUPTIONS.

DO WE NEED A LINE ON THE FLOOR HERE TOO?

YOU TELL ME.

STAY OUT OF OUR WAY.

BASICS. WRIST STRAIGHT, THUMB AT ELEVEN O'CLOCK. DON'T OVER ROTATE...

I'D NEVER BEEN TO BOARDING SCHOOL BEFORE.

IT'S NOT LIKE IN THE MOVIES.

HAVE YOU SEEN MY FENCING SHOES?

FIRST, THERE IS *ZERO* PRIVACY.

ANYONE GOT ANY SNACKS?

SO TO SOLVE FOR X YOU HAVE TO FIRST DIVIDE BY FIVE, THEN...

WHICH IS TOUGH BECAUSE YOU'RE ALWAYS GETTING CHANGED.

NO, THAT'S THE SCHOOL SWEATER. YOU NEED THE RUGBY SHIRT AND LONG SOCKS FOR SPORTS CLASS.

BELLS RING ALL THE TIME. TO START CLASS. TO FINISH CLASS.

DING DING

TO WAKE US UP IN THE MORNING. TO ANNOUNCE LIGHTS-OUT AT NIGHT.

DING DING

MNNGHRRHH.

FOR STUDY HALL. FOR DINNER. FOR SCHOOL ASSEMBLY--

STOP. THAT'S A RUGBY SHIRT. FOR SCHOOL ASSEMBLY, YOU NEED THE BUTTON-UP, TIE, AND SCHOOL BLAZER.

DING DING

MY DORMITORY IS CALLED CASTELLO. MOST OF THE KINGS ROW FENCERS BOARD HERE.

BOBBY'S ACROSS THE HALL. HE ROOMS WITH A GUY CALLED DANTE.

THEY'RE ALWAYS TOGETHER.

CHICKEN.

APPLE.

SWAP!

even though it's a rich school, the food still sucks.

THE TEAM CAPTAIN IS THREE DOORS DOWN THE HALL. HE ROOMS WITH THE SCHOOL PLAYBOY.

THE CURRENT FENCING TEAM EATS TOGETHER.

Captain

playboy

KALLY AND TANNER ARE ROOM DOWNSTAIRS. KALLY KEEPS TANNER IN LINE.

AND **THIS GUY** IS MY ROOMMATE.

EVERYTHING IS REALLY STRICT.

LIGHTS OUT IS AT 9:30? BUT YOU GUYS SNEAK OUT, RIGHT?

...

...

SOMETIMES I DO MY HOMEWORK SECRETLY WITH A FLASHLIGHT UNDER THE BLANKET.

THE GUYS ARE SURPRISINGLY NICE. ESPECIALLY KALLY.

I JUST GOT A CARE PACKAGE! COME SHARE IT!

CHOCOLATE! IT'S BEEN SO LONG...

BEEF JERKY!

ARE THOSE TWO-MINUTE NOODLES?

FRUIT AND MUESLI BARS GO IN THE "EAT WHEN DESPERATE" PILE.

BUT UNDER IT ALL, EVERYONE'S TENSE, BECAUSE IN THE END...

ONLY **THREE** PEOPLE CAN MAKE THE TEAM.

THE MATCH-UPS FOR THE TRYOUT TOURNAMENT ARE POSTED!

KINGS ROW FENCING TEAM TRYOUTS
ROUND ROBIN MATCHUPS

MY FIRST BOUT IS AGAINST THE CAPTAIN?! IT'S GOING TO BE A WIPEOUT.

HEY LOOK, I'M FENCING ZERO. EASY WIN!

DON'T CALL ME THAT!

I'M FENCING SEIJI. GOOD. I CAN'T WAIT TO TEACH THAT ARROGANT FRESHMAN A LESSON.

IS THAT REALLY WHAT YOU THINK IS GOING TO HAPPEN?

THE TOURNAMENT IS ROUND ROBIN STYLE, SO EACH FENCER HAS TO FENCE EVERY OTHER FENCER ONCE.

WE'LL ALL HAVE TO FENCE SEIJI EVENTUALLY.

INCLUDING ME.

I'LL FINALLY GET TO FACE HIM AGAIN, LIKE I PROMISED.

I JUST HAVE TO FENCE EUGENE FIRST.

TRYOUTS, DAY ONE.

AIDEN!

DO I KNOW YOU?

I... WE, LAST NIGHT...

OH, RIGHT. WHAT WAS YOUR NAME AGAIN?

YOU DON'T REMEMBER MY NAME?

IF YOU'RE TRYING OUT FOR THE TEAM, LET ME SAVE YOU SOME TIME. YOU'RE NOT GOOD ENOUGH TO MAKE IT.

W-WHAT?

I DON'T SLEEP WITH GUYS ON THE TEAM.

BUT--I THOUGHT WE HAD SOMETH--

LISTEN, IT WAS FUN FOR A NIGHT, BUT LET'S NOT PRETEND IT WAS MORE THAN IT WAS.

WE DON'T EVEN KNOW EACH OTHER.

THAT WAS COLD.

ANOTHER AIDEN CASUALTY.

HE SHOULD COME WITH A WARNING.

JAY! IGNORE HIM. FOCUS ON YOUR OWN MATCH.

THIS IS YOUR CHANCE TO FENCE. DON'T LET AIDEN SCREW IT UP FOR YOU.

HE DOESN'T CARE ABOUT--

SHUT UP! WHAT DO YOU KNOW ABOUT US?

I KNOW AIDEN. I'VE KNOWN HIM SINCE WE WERE FIVE.

HARVARD, HONESTLY. WHY DO YOU WASTE YOUR TIME ON THOSE LOSERS?

YOU KNOW HE HAS NO CHANCE TO MAKE THE TEAM.

JAY'S NOT A LOSER.

JAY! THAT WAS HIS NAME.

WINNER!
SEIJI KATAYAMA

SEIJI'S AMAZING!

BOBBY'S RIGHT. SEIJI'S EVEN BETTER THAN HE WAS LAST YEAR.

TCH! WHY DOES SUCH A HUGE JERK HAVE TO BE SO GOOD AT FENCING?

IT'S TOTALLY UNREASONABLE.

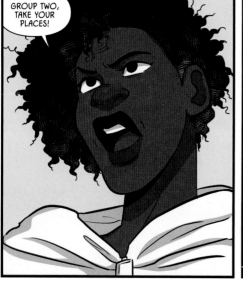

GROUP TWO, TAKE YOUR PLACES!

SEIJI WON HIS FIRST MATCH. I HAVE TO DO THE SAME.

WHICH BOUT SHOULD WE WATCH? SINCE AIDEN'S NOT FENCING RIGHT NOW.

HOW ABOUT WE CHECK OUT THE FRESHMAN WHO'S HERE ON SCHOLARSHIP?

NICHOLAS? NO WAY, HE'S TERRIBLE!

I HEARD HE FENCED SEIJI AT REGIONALS AND LOST.

YEAH, BUT THEN HE CAME HERE DETERMINED TO BEAT HIM.

EVERY BOY IN THE UNDER-16s IS CHASING SEIJI.

BUT IT'S A ONE-SIDED RELATIONSHIP.

A FENCER AS GOOD AS SEIJI DOESN'T THINK TWICE ABOUT A GUY LIKE NICHOLAS.

...SO WHY IS SEIJI WATCHING HIS MATCH?

IT'S THE FIRST DAY OF TRYOUTS. EVERYONE IS NERVOUS.

THEY SHOW IT IN DIFFERENT WAYS.

"SOME EXTERNAL."

"FOR SOME IT'S INTERNAL.

RRRRAAAHHH!

"SOME PUT THEMSELVES UNDER MORE PRESSURE THAN OTHERS.

"AND EVERYONE IS WATCHING.

"EVEN YOU, SEIJI."

I'VE BEATEN PEOPLE LIKE EUGENE BEFORE.

I CAN SEE HIS MISTAKES. I CAN ANTICIPATE HIS ATTACKS.

IF I CAN JUST FENCE NORMALLY...

HIT

YOU'VE BEEN POORLY TRAINED, AND YOU'VE LEARNED A LOT OF BAD HABITS.

YOUR TECHNIQUE IS THE WEAKEST OF THE BOYS HERE.

HE'S OVERTHINKING.

MAYBE IT'S THE PRESSURE. SOMETHING'S GOT IN HIS HEAD.

HE NEEDS TO JUST RELAX AND FENCE THE WAY HE USUALLY DOES.

BUT FENCING THE WAY YOU USUALLY DO...

NO MATTER WHAT COACH SAYS.

THE CLASS IS SPLIT IN HALF.

AND THOSE WHO HAVE A WIN.

THOSE WHO HAVE A LOSS.

SEIJI.

HIS HITS ARE HARD.

REALLY HARD.

I REMEMBER. I WAS BRUISED ALL OVER.

DO THEY HURT?

OW! DON'T POKE THEM!

HEY, NICHOLAS, DID YOU KNOW SEIJI WAS WATCHING YOUR MATCH?

PERFECT. THE ICING ON THE CAKE.

108

108

I THOUGHT YOU'D BE USED TO LOSING.

FOR ONCE, COULD YOU JUST--

YOU KNOW WHAT? I'M OUT OF HERE.

NICHOLAS? WHERE ARE YOU GOING? IT'S ALMOST CURFEW.

TRYOUTS, DAY TWO.

HEY, KALLY! GOING TO WIN AGAIN TODAY?

ACTUALLY, I LOST YESTERDAY! 15-7 TO AIDEN.

YOU LOST TO AIDEN?! BUT HE'S NEVER AT PRACTICE.

I KNOW HE WAS TECHNICALLY ON THE TEAM WITH YOU, BUT HE NEVER SHOWS UP TO BOUTS OR ANYTHING...

IF AIDEN HAD BOTHERED TURNING UP TO ANY OF OUR MATCHES, WE'D HAVE DONE A LOT BETTER AT STATE LAST YEAR.

IF YOU FINISH EARLY, YOU'LL GET TO SEE AIDEN'S FIRST BOUT.

HE'S FENCING SEIJI.

HAHA, HOW DID YOU KNOW I WAS GOING TO WATCH THAT BOUT?

EVERYONE, GATHER ROUND! TODAY IS THE SECOND DAY OF TRYOUTS--

WHERE'S NICHOLAS?

I HAVEN'T SEEN HIM SINCE LAST NIGHT.

IF HE'S LATE FOR HIS MATCH HE'LL GET A LOSS BY DEFAULT...

Issue #05
On Sale Now!

DISCOVER
ALL THE HITS

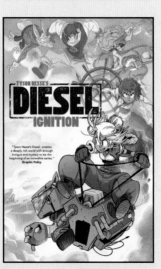

Lumberjanes
Noelle Stevenson, Shannon Watters,
Grace Ellis, Brooklyn Allen, and Others
Volume 1: Beware the Kitten Holy
ISBN: 978-1-60886-687-8 | $14.99 US
Volume 2: Friendship to the Max
ISBN: 978-1-60886-737-0 | $14.99 US
Volume 3: A Terrible Plan
ISBN: 978-1-60886-803-2 | $14.99 US
Volume 4: Out of Time
ISBN: 978-1-60886-860-5 | $14.99 US
Volume 5: Band Together
ISBN: 978-1-60886-919-0 | $14.99 US

Giant Days
John Allison, Lissa Treiman, Max Sarin
Volume 1
ISBN: 978-1-60886-789-9 | $9.99 US
Volume 2
ISBN: 978-1-60886-804-9 | $14.99 US
Volume 3
ISBN: 978-1-60886-851-3 | $14.99 US

Jonesy
Sam Humphries, Caitlin Rose Boyle
Volume 1
ISBN: 978-1-60886-883-4 | $9.99 US
Volume 2
ISBN: 978-1-60886-999-2 | $14.99 US

Slam!
Pamela Ribon, Veronica Fish,
Brittany Peer
Volume 1
ISBN: 978-1-68415-004-5 | $14.99 US

Goldie Vance
Hope Larson, Brittney Williams
Volume 1
ISBN: 978-1-60886-898-8 | $9.99 US
Volume 2
ISBN: 978-1-60886-974-9 | $14.99 US

The Backstagers
James Tynion IV, Rian Sygh
Volume 1
ISBN: 978-1-60886-993-0 | $14.99 US

Tyson Hesse's Diesel: Ignition
Tyson Hesse
ISBN: 978-1-60886-907-7 | $14.99 US

Coady & The Creepies
Liz Prince, Amanda Kirk,
Hannah Fisher
ISBN: 978-1-68415-029-8 | $14.99 US

AVAILABLE AT YOUR LOCAL COMICS SHOP AND BOOKSTORE
WWW.**BOOM-STUDIOS**.COM